Ocarina Choo-C[barcode]
GW00381301

A beginner's guide to the 4 hole alto ocarina

2: Learning More By Alison Hedger

The following notes are used in this book: **D, E, F♯, G, A, B, C♮, C♯ and D'**

This book is for young children in particular, but also for those young-at-heart. Progress is gradual with lots of tunes to play. The approach is fun, and the recognition of traditional notation should become like a second language. It is not a good idea to write the note names on the music – it is preferable for children to learn their notes.

Say and clap the rhythmic patterns of the tunes (using the words given) whilst looking at the written music. This way, the relation of note values will be gradually assimilated.

The object of OCARINA CHOO-CHOO is for children to play music well, as soon as possible. Children should attempt to produce a good tone from the outset, and learn to play together with regard for others in the group.

The optional CD contains full backing tracks of many tunes to play along with.

© Copyright 2000 Chester Music Limited
Designed by Chloë Alexander • Illustrations by Jan McCafferty • Music setting by Paul Ewers
Printed in Great Britain by Caligraving Limited, Thetford, Norfolk

Chester Music Limited
(A division of Music Sales Limited)
8/9 Frith Street, London W1V 5TZ

395

It is not a good idea for children to be reliant on following fingering diagrams.

It is preferable, even for young children, to recognise which notes to play by their position on the stave.

The drawback with reading diagrams is that the rhythm of the notes is secondary and more often than not ignored.

By looking at traditional notation, both pitch and rhythm are assimilated from the beginning.

Points of theory to be found in this book, and tunes to play using them

Dotted crotchet ♩. ♪	pages 20, 21, 26, 28, 29, 30
Key signature	page 11
Ostinato	pages 21, 23, 26, 32
Part playing	pages 13, 18, 21, 29
Rests for a single beat 𝄽	pages 3, 4, 15, 18, 23, 26-31
for two counts ▬	pages 4, 6, 8, 11, 18
Rounds	pages 15, 23, 27, 32
Slurs ⌒	pages 19, 20, 21, 24, 25, 27, 29-32
Staccato ♩̇ ♩̇ ♩̇	pages 8, 9, 15, 18, 21, 31, 32
Ties ‿	pages 20, 25, 29

Doris the Dog

Ezra the Elephant

F♯rankie the Frog

Gloria the Goat

Agnes the Anteater

Bevin the Beetle

C♯lover the Chicken

D'an the Driver

C♮ has no character

A reminder of all the notes learnt in Book 1: Getting Started

Can you play them all? And can you recognise which line or space they have on the stave?

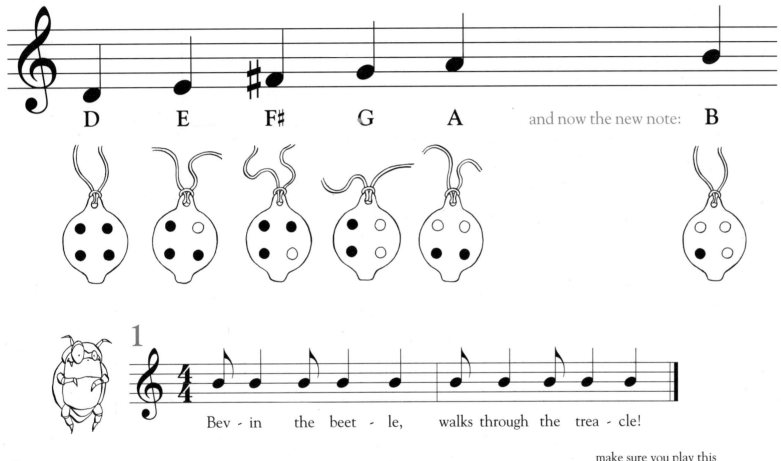

D   E   F♯   G   A   and now the new note: B

On the middle line

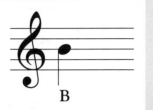

B

B

Cover only one hole – the biggest one! Don't forget to keep your third fingers as 'balancers'.

1

Bev - in   the beet - le,   walks through the trea - cle!

make sure you play this note for 3 whole beats!

2

Rest,   2,   3,   rest,   2,   3,   rest,   2,   3,   1,   2,   3

3

B and G

B   G

G

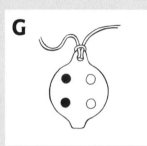

Tongue each note by making your tongue 'say' du.

1

Hop a-long my friend. Don't for-get to lend me some mon-ey soon, for a blue bal-loon.

2

La - zy, ha - zy days of sun, now the sum - mer has be - gun.

3

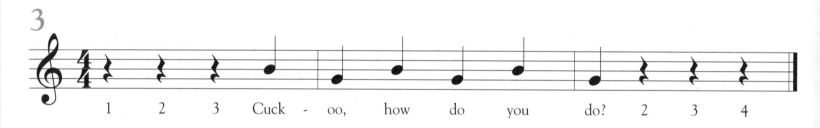

1   2   3   Cuck - oo, how do you do? 2   3   4

𝄽 = a one beat silence, or rest

▬ = a two beat rest

4

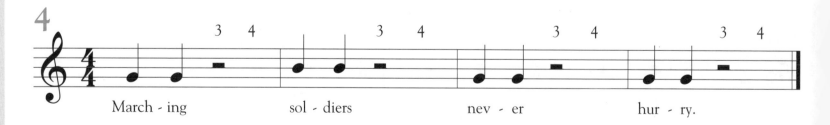

March - ing sol - diers nev - er hur - ry.

4

1

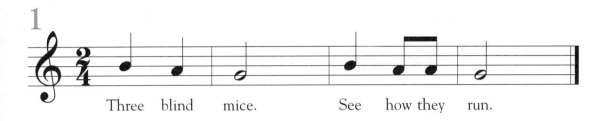

Three blind mice. See how they run.

2

O-ca-ri-na choo-choo, red and blue. Pas-sen-gers please line up, make a queue.

A Welsh folk-tune called Suo-Gân

3

True or false?

	True	False
• A one beat rest looks like this 𝄽	✓	
• A two beat rest looks like this ▬	✓	
• 𝄞 this is called a Trombone Clef		✓
• A cross, ✗, is used to tell you when to take a breath		✓

Answers

A one beat rest looks like this 𝄽

A two beat rest looks like this ▬

𝄞 this is called a TREBLE clef

A tick, ✓ is used to tell you when to take a breath

B, A and G

B   A   G

A

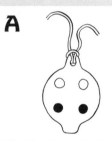

Alternate between B and A, sounding like a siren. This not only sounds good, but is fun to play!

Don't forget to play 'wibbly-wobbly' – but keep your third fingers (balancers) still! (See Book 1: Getting Started, page 2)

5

E, G and B

Every
Good
Boy

Don't blow your ocarina too hard, or you will play out of tune.

1

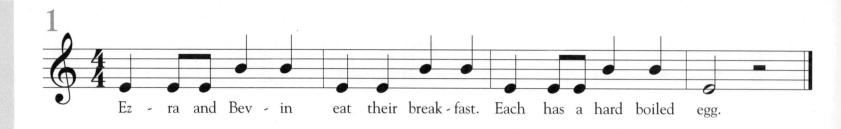

Ez - ra and Bev - in eat their break - fast. Each has a hard boiled egg.

2

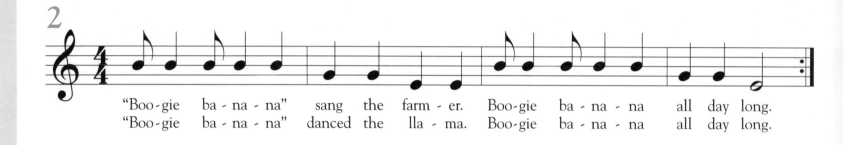

"Boo - gie ba - na - na" sang the farm - er. Boo - gie ba - na - na all day long.
"Boo - gie ba - na - na" danced the lla - ma. Boo - gie ba - na - na all day long.

3

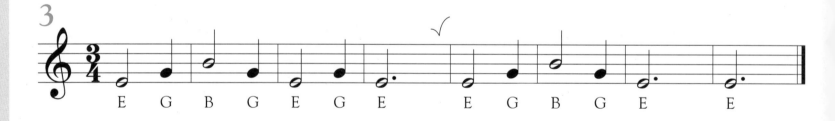

E   G   B   G   E   G   E   E   G   B   G   E   E

4

Ev - ery good boy gets East - er eggs.

1

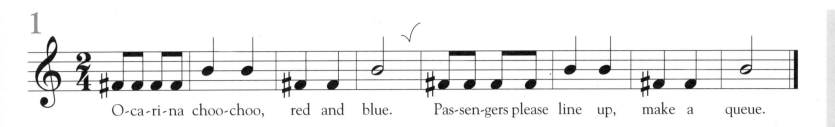

O-ca-ri-na choo-choo, red and blue. Pas-sen-gers please line up, make a queue.

2

Hel - lo there, Mis - ter Bear. Have you a - ny buns to spare?

3

Ev - ery day child - ren say "Is it time to go and play?"

4

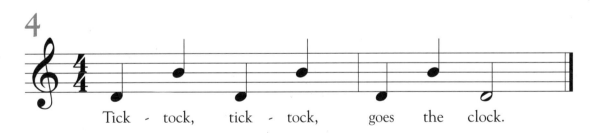

Tick - tock, tick - tock, goes the clock.

5

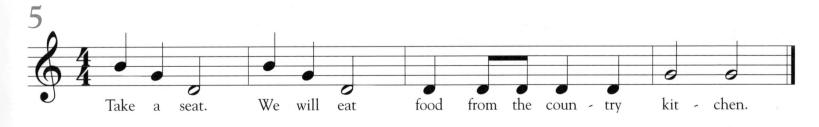

Take a seat. We will eat food from the coun - try kit - chen.

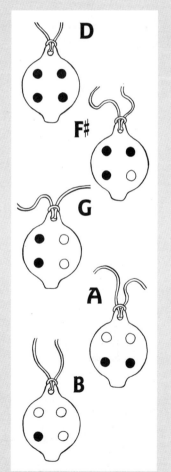

Top D'

Top D'

D'

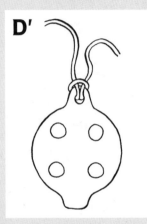

All the holes
are uncovered

D   D'

How many finger
holes are covered to
play low D?

1

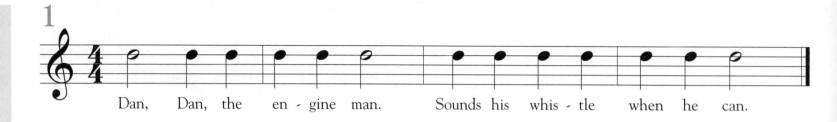

Dan, Dan, the en - gine man. Sounds his whis - tle when he can.

These little dots tell you to make your tonguing short and spikey,
so that each note is crisp. We call this STACCATO.

2

Toot - toot.   Toot - toot.   Toot - toot - toot - toot - toot - toot.

3

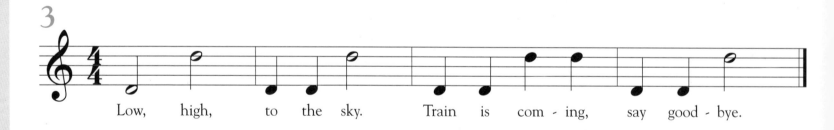

Low, high, to the sky. Train is com - ing, say good - bye.

4

Do - ris and Dan, Do - ris and Dan, they can cook in a fry - ing pan.

8

1

Clo-ver the chick-en is rea-dy to peck. Each time we see her she's stretch-ing her neck!

2

Cluck, cluck. Hi, it's me! Clo-ver the chick-en drink-ing tea.

Don't 'overblow' and keep tonguing 'du' on every note.

3

O-ca-ri-na choo-choo, red and blue. Pas-sen-gers please line up, make a queue.

4

Fin-ger up, and fin-ger down. We'll dance like this; go round and round!

C sharp

C sharp

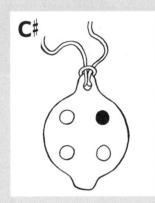
C#

B   C sharp

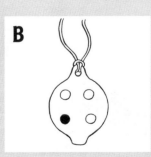
B

Mini Quiz

You choose a note, and finger it.

Your friend has to name which note it is.

- Write the letter name underneath each note

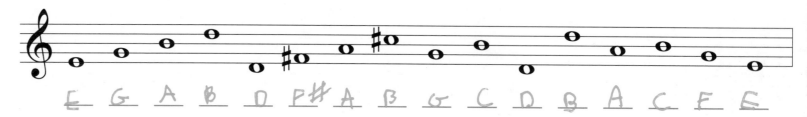

E G A B D F# A B G C D B A C F E

- This time, you carefully draw the notes onto the stave above each note name

E G G B A G D A D' B E D D F# B D' G A E C#

- Write in the letter name of the note that belongs to each character (if you get stuck, have a peep at page 2)

1

Clo - ver and Frank - ie both have sharps. Sharps look like rail tracks cross - ing.

Both can hang their sharps on the stave, then lots of cross - ings we will save!

Can you see what I see?

Frankie's sharp goes on the top line
Clover has hers a bit lower

Frankie's Clover's

2

Clo - ver and Frank - ie both have sharps. Sharps look like rail tracks cross - ing.

Both can hang their sharps on the stave, then lots of cross - ings we will save!

When the sharps are placed at the beginning of the stave, this is called the KEY SIGNATURE.

C♯ F♯

C sharp F sharp

C♯

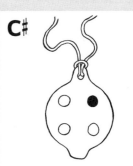

F♯

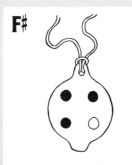

 a sharp

Tunes 1 and 2 are the same: just written out **differently, that's all!**

11

Colour in the finger holes which need to be covered to make each note. (One of them doesn't have any holes covered. Which one?)

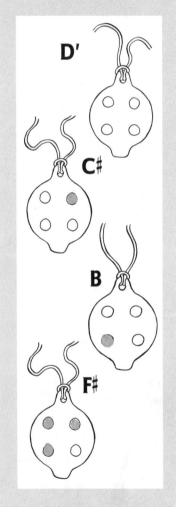

D'

C#

B

F#

1

1. What a to-do, we're off to Crewe. Choo-choo, choo-choo!
2. Trund-ling a-long, we'll sing a song. Choo-choo, choo-choo!

2

Clo-ver pecks in the air, she pecks at the ground.

Clo-ver scratch-es and she clucks as she struts a-round.

3

Cob-bler, cob-bler, mend my shoe, get it done by half past two.

If you mend my shoe to-day, then a pen-ny I will pay.

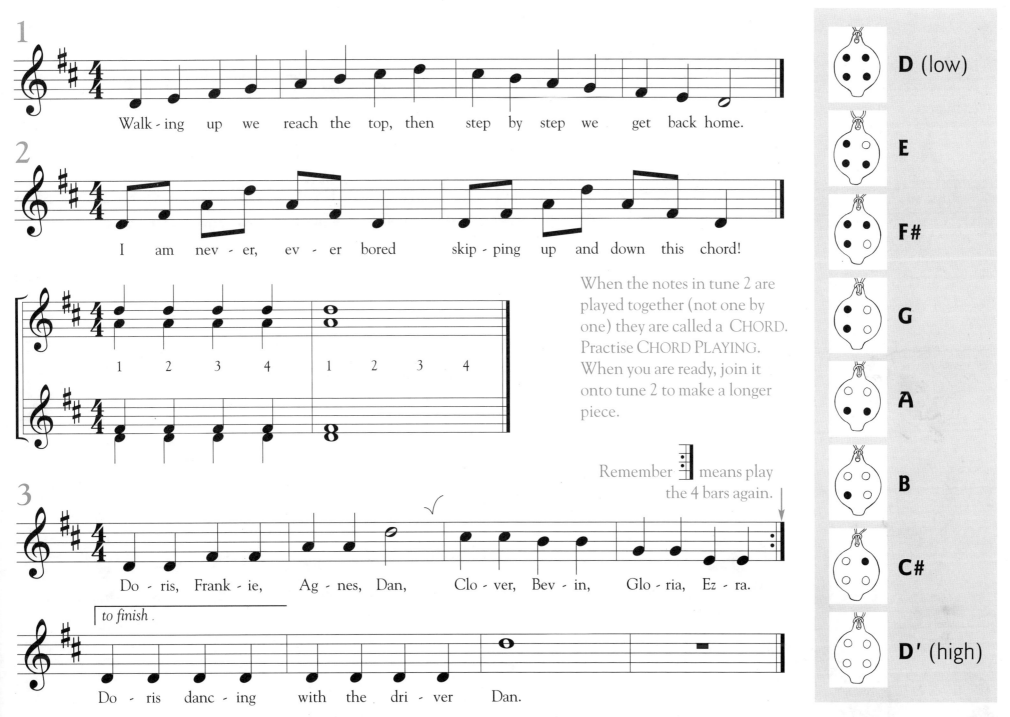

When the notes in tune 2 are played together (not one by one) they are called a CHORD. Practise CHORD PLAYING. When you are ready, join it onto tune 2 to make a longer piece.

Remember means play the 4 bars again.

13

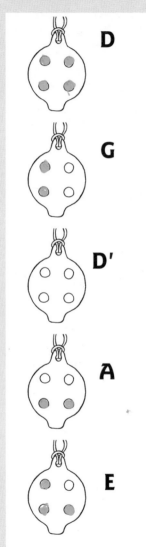
1

1, 2, 3, 4. You must al - ways shut the door, then we won't be sit - ting here, freez - ing cold!

Are you remembering to tongue on every note?

2

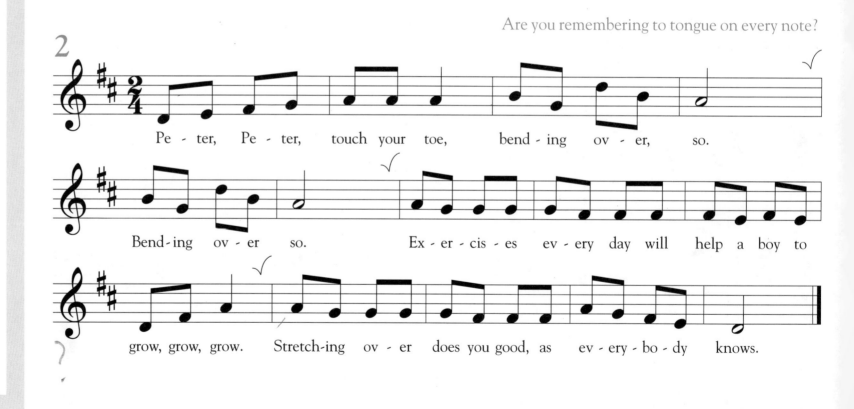

Pe - ter, Pe - ter, touch your toe, bend - ing ov - er, so.

Bend - ing ov - er so. Ex - er - cis - es ev - ery day will help a boy to

grow, grow, grow. Stretch - ing ov - er does you good, as ev - ery - bo - dy knows.

A Round

1

① Can you see the snow float - ing down from on high?

② Pret - ty sight, shin - ing white, fall - ing from the sky.

To play this as a simple round, the second part
starts half-way through (after the breath mark).

2

We must hur - ry to the sta - tion, the train must be near. We must

hur - ry to the sta - tion, the train is now here!

It's also possible to play this round with up to 8 parts. Each part joins in after the previous part has played 'Can you see the...'

15

Don't forget to
tongue each note

Can you name these
notes from the
fingerings given:

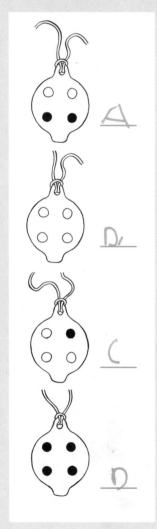

A

D

C

D

1

See saw, Mar - jo - rie Daw, John - nie shall have a new mas - ter.

He shall have but a pen - ny a day, be - cause he can't work an - y fast - er!

Negro Spiritual

2

1. Go   tell it on the moun - tain, ov - er the hills and far a - way.
2. Go   tell it to my peo - ple, ov - er the hills and far a - way.

Go   tell it on the moun - tain, that Je - sus Christ is Lord.
Go   tell it to my peo - ple, that Je - sus Christ is Lord.

1

Introduction

Down at the bot-tom of the deep blue sea
catch - ing fish - es for my tea. Down to the bot - tom
you must go. E. I. E. I. Oh!

2

European Folk Tune

Try a rhythmic ostinato using percussion instruments playing:

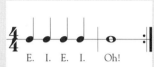

E. I. E. I. Oh!

17

Playing In Parts

The Dripping Tap

Sung to the words:
Will you please stop that dripping tap!
Will you please stop that dripping tap!
Will you please stop that dripping tap!
Thanks!

Which words have the staccato notes?

Up to now you have always tongued each note,
but sometimes notes are slurred together, using a slur sign

Only tongue the first note in a slur. Keep blowing and change the fingers for the next note.
Practise the following short exercises – you'll soon get the right idea!

a du, du, du, du   **b** du —— du ——   **c** du — du — du

1

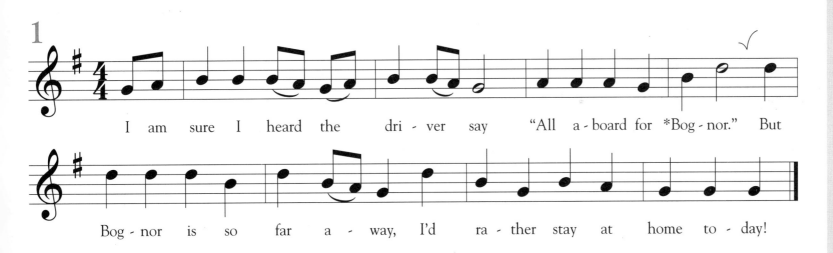

I am sure I heard the dri - ver say "All a - board for *Bog - nor." But

Bog - nor is so far a - way, I'd ra - ther stay at home to - day!

* This could be
Cardiff, Forfar, or
anywhere else that
fits!

2 A scale with more slurs for you to try.

19

How many slurs are there in tune 1?

Answer: 4

How many ties are there in tune 2?

Answer: 2

1. I would love a cup of tea and bis - cuits.
2. I am sit - ting un - der - neath the fir tree,

If it's not much trou - ble, bring it out here.
think - ing how I'd like a cup of sweet tea!

There is another sign in music which looks like a slur ⌣ but is really quite different.

The **tie** ties up note values together.

Pull the string a - gain. Tie it tight.

Clap the following:

1   2 and   1   2

Now clap this pattern which is almost the same, but the first two notes are tied together:

1   2 and   1   2

Another way of writing the same pattern is:

1   2 and   1   2

20

1 German tune

2

Part 1 / Part 2:

My fa-vourite is choc - olate and can - dy floss.

This is an ostinato to fit with tune 2:

I like sweet - ies. I like sweet - ies.

Also play the ostinato rhythm on a drum or woodblock:

1 2 and 3 4 1 2 and 3 4

The ostinato makes an excellent introduction – play it twice before the other parts come in.

C natural

C

This new note is C without a #

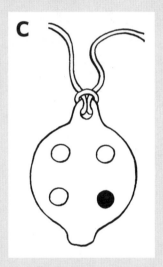

C

Listen to the difference between C and C# :

C#

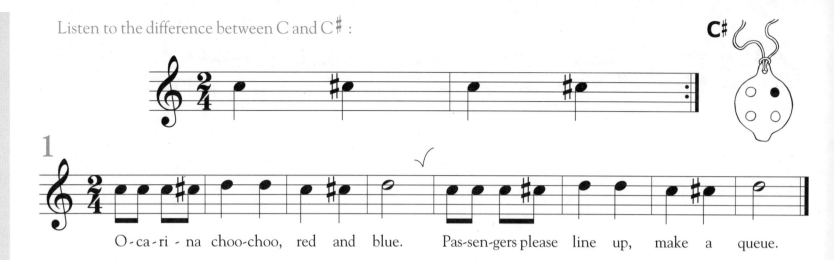

1

O - ca - ri - na choo-choo, red and blue. Pas-sen-gers please line up, make a queue.

A natural sign ♮ is placed in front of the note C if it is needed to cancel out the sharp.

If there is no # sign in front of the note C, and there is not a C# 'hung up' at the beginning of the stave after the 𝄞, then PLAY C NATURAL.

British tune

2

Hot cross buns. Hot cross buns. One a pen - ny, two a pen - ny, hot cross buns.

This is the new note: C natural.

1

Bohemian tune

I've been travel-ling all day long up - on this choo-choo train.
I am tired and I am hun-gry. Do you feel the same?

I'll be pleased to see my friend, when we reach our jour-ney's end!

I've been travel-ling all day long up - on this choo-choo train.

A Round

2

Traditional

① For health and strength and dai-ly food we thank you, O, our God.

② For health and strength we thank you God.

For health and strength.

When there is just one ♯ in the key signature, this is Frankie's F sharp.

All the C notes will be C natural.

An ostinato to play with the round.

23

1

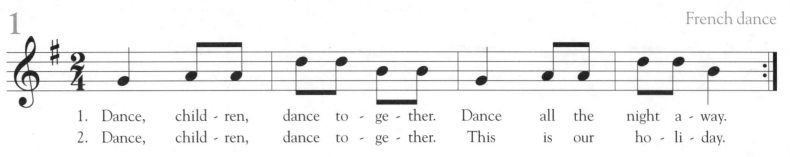

1. Dance, child - ren, dance to - ge - ther. Dance all the night a - way.
2. Dance, child - ren, dance to - ge - ther. This is our ho - li - day.

2

Hush, lit - tle ba - by, don't say a word. Mum-my's going to buy you a mock-ing bird.

3

European tune

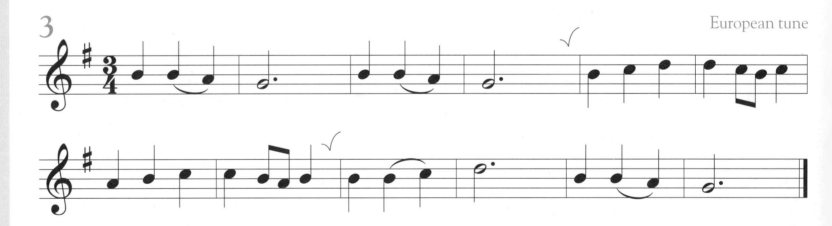

Are there any slurs or ties in tune 3?

Answer: Yes, 4 slurs
(see pages 20 and 21)

24

2
1. Creep - ing   up   and   creep - ing   down.
2. Listen - ing   to   this   spook - y   sound!

German tune

3
Mar - ket Har - borough here we come — we are look - ing for some fun.

All will see   you and me,   in a ca - fé—— drink - ing tea.

Scottish dance

4

Always have a good look at the key signature before you play, to see if C natural or C sharp is needed.

C
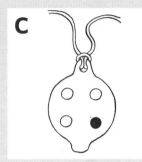

C#
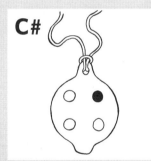

Can you name these notes from the fingerings given:

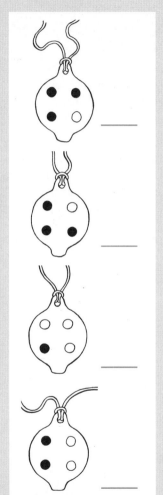

Try adding some hand-drums, guiros, woodblocks or bells to *Alison's Jig*.

1

Have you seen the muf - fin man, the muf - fin man, the muf - fin man?

Have you seen the muf - fin man who lives in Dru - ry Lane?

Yes, I've seen the muf - fin man, the muf - fin man, the muf - fin man.

Yes, I've seen the muf - fin man who lives in Dru - ry Lane.

An ostinato to play with song 1

2 Alison's Jig

An ostinato to play with tune 2

1

My dame hath a lame, tame, crane. My dame hath a crane that is lame.

Pray, gen-tle Jane, let my dame's lame, tame crane, feed and come home a - gain!

2

Bob - by Shaf - toe's gone to sea,— sil - ver buck - les on his knee.—

He'll come back and mar - ry me,— bon - ny Bob - by Shaf - toe. *(End)*

Bob - by Shaf - toe's bright and fair, comb - ing down his yel - low hair.

(go back to beginning)

He's my own for ev - er - more. Bon - ny Bob - by Shaf - toe.

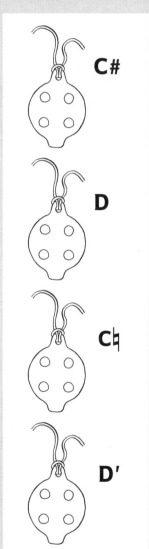

Colour in the finger holes which need to be covered to make each note:

C#

D

C♮

D'

1   Hungarian tune

2   Thomas Morley

Now is the month of May - ing, when mer - ry lads are play - ing. Fa, la, la, la, la, la,

la, la, la. Fa, la, la, la, la, la, la. Each with his bon - ny lass a - danc - ing on the

these 2 bars make an excellent introduction

grass. Fa, la, la, la, la. Fa, la, la, la, la, la, la, la, la, la, la, la.

3   **Sadly**

1 Gently

Part 1 / Part 2

Part 1 / Part 2

2

Sal - ly go round the stars. Sal - ly go round the moon.

Sal - ly go round the chim - ney pots on a Sat - ur - day af - ter - noon.

Some-one's in the kit-chen with the dri - ver, some-one's in the kit-chen I know.

Some-one's in the kit-chen with the dri - ver strum-ming on the old ban - jo.

Fee, fie, fid - dle di, doh! Fee, fie, fid - dle di doh. Fee, fie,

(with voices)

fid - dle di, doh! Strum-ming on the old ban - jo!

(stamp, stamp)
(clap, clap)

1

Sit - ting on the choo - choo train are the cha - rac - ter a - ni - mals, and a man!

Do - ris, Ez - ra, Frank - ie, Glo - ri - a, Ag - nes, Bev - in, Clo - ver, Dan.

2

① ②

Choo - choo train is quite full up and there's no room. There's no room.

③ ④

Catch a train to - mor - row. Catch a train to - mor - row. Tick - ets please! Tick - ets please!

Have fun actually being the choo-choo train.
Take it in turns to line up in single file.
Make your arms into big, turning wheels, and off you go as the music is played.
Make a snaking pattern all around the room, 'letting off steam' as you go –
'choo-choo-chooing' in time with the music.

An ostinato for song 2:

Choo - choo train!

Use the ostinato as your introduction.

32